OFFICIAL SQA PAST PAPERS
WITH ANSWERS

INTERMEDIATE 2 | UNITS 1, 2 & 3

MATHEMATICS
2007-2011

Publisher's Note

We are delighted to bring you the 2011 Past Papers and you will see that we have changed the format from previous editions. As part of our environmental awareness strategy, we have attempted to make these new editions as sustainable as possible.
To do this, we have printed on white paper and bound the answer sections into the book. This not only allows us to use significantly less paper but we are also, for the first time, able to source all the materials from sustainable sources.

We hope you like the new editions and by purchasing this product, you are not only supporting an independent Scottish publishing company but you are also, in the International Year of Forests, not contributing to the destruction of the world's forests.

Thank you for your support and please see the following websites for more information to support the above statement –

www.fsc-uk.org

www.loveforests.com

© Scottish Qualifications Authority
All rights reserved. Copying prohibited. No part of this publication may be reproduced, stored in a retrieval system, or transmitted in any form or by any means, electronic, mechanical, photocopying, recording or otherwise.

First exam published in 2007.
Published by Bright Red Publishing Ltd, 6 Stafford Street, Edinburgh EH3 7AU
tel: 0131 220 5804 fax: 0131 220 6710 info@brightredpublishing.co.uk www.brightredpublishing.co.uk

ISBN 978-1-84948-202-8

A CIP Catalogue record for this book is available from the British Library.

Bright Red Publishing is grateful to the copyright holders, as credited on the final page of the Question Section, for permission to use their material. Every effort has been made to trace the copyright holders and to obtain their permission for the use of copyright material. Bright Red Publishing will be happy to receive information allowing us to rectify any error or omission in future editions.

[BLANK PAGE]

X100/201

NATIONAL
QUALIFICATIONS
2007

TUESDAY, 15 MAY
1.00 PM – 1.45 PM

MATHEMATICS
INTERMEDIATE 2
Units 1, 2 and 3
Paper 1
(Non-calculator)

Read carefully

1 **You may NOT use a calculator.**

2 Full credit will be given only where the solution contains appropriate working.

3 Square-ruled paper Is providod.

FORMULAE LIST

The roots of $ax^2 + bx + c = 0$ are $x = \dfrac{-b \pm \sqrt{(b^2 - 4ac)}}{2a}$

Sine rule: $\dfrac{a}{\sin A} = \dfrac{b}{\sin B} = \dfrac{c}{\sin C}$

Cosine rule: $a^2 = b^2 + c^2 - 2bc \cos A$ or $\cos A = \dfrac{b^2 + c^2 - a^2}{2bc}$

Area of a triangle: $\text{Area} = \frac{1}{2} ab \sin C$

Volume of a sphere: $\text{Volume} = \frac{4}{3} \pi r^3$

Volume of a cone: $\text{Volume} = \frac{1}{3} \pi r^2 h$

Volume of a cylinder: $\text{Volume} = \pi r^2 h$

Standard deviation: $s = \sqrt{\dfrac{\sum(x - \bar{x})^2}{n-1}} = \sqrt{\dfrac{\sum x^2 - (\sum x)^2 / n}{n-1}}$, where n is the sample size.

Marks

ALL questions should be attempted.

1. The table below shows the results of a survey of First Year pupils.

	Wearing a blazer	*Not wearing a blazer*
Boys	40	22
Girls	29	9

What is the probability that a pupil, chosen at random from this sample, will be a girl wearing a blazer?

1

2.

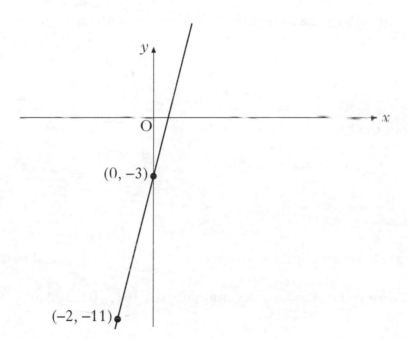

Find the equation of the straight line passing through the points (0, –3) and (–2, –11).

3

[Turn over

Marks

3. A tin of tuna is in the shape of a cylinder.

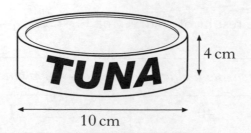

It has diameter 10 centimetres and height 4 centimetres.

Calculate its volume.

Take $\pi = 3\cdot14$.   2

4. Find the point of intersection of the straight lines with equations $x + 2y = -5$ and $3x - y = 13$.   4

5. Multiply out the brackets and collect like terms.

$$(x + 3)(x^2 + 4x - 12)$$ 3

6. (*a*) Show that the standard deviation of 1, 1, 1, 2 and 5 is equal to $\sqrt{3}$.   3

(*b*) **Write down** the standard deviation of 101, 101, 101, 102 and 105.   1

Marks

7. The graph shown below is part of the parabola with equation $y = 8x - x^2$.

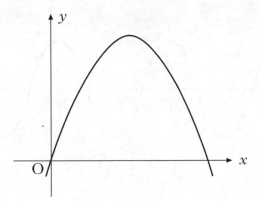

(a) By factorising $8x - x^2$, find the roots of the equation

$$8x - x^2 = 0.$$ **2**

(b) State the equation of the axis of symmetry of the parabola.   **1**

(c) Find the coordinates of the turning point.   **2**

8. Given that

$$\cos 60° = 0.5,$$

what is the value of $\cos 240°$?   **1**

9. A right-angled triangle is shown below.

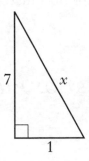

Using Pythagoras' Theorem, find x.

Express your answer as a surd in its simplest form.   **3**

[Turn over for Questions 10 and 11 on *Page six*

Marks

10. (a) Part of the graph of $y = \cos ax°$ is shown below.

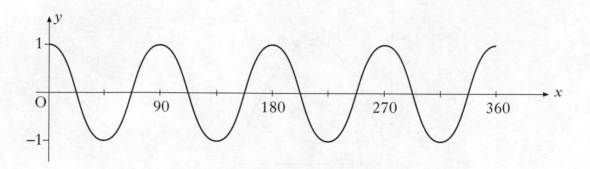

State the value of a.

1

(b) Part of the graph of $y = \tan bx°$ is shown below.

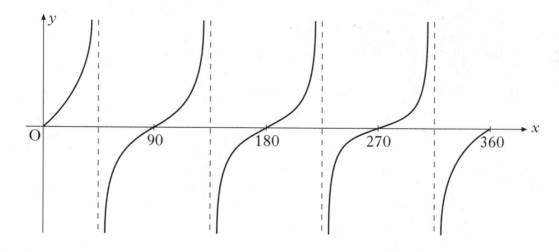

State the value of b.

1

11. A straight line is represented by the equation $y = ax + b$.

Sketch a possible straight line graph to illustrate this equation when $a = 0$ and $b > 0$.

2

[END OF QUESTION PAPER]

X100/203

| NATIONAL QUALIFICATIONS 2007 | TUESDAY, 15 MAY 2.05 PM – 3.35 PM | MATHEMATICS INTERMEDIATE 2 Units 1, 2 and 3 Paper 2 |

Read carefully

1 **Calculators may be used in this paper.**

2 Full credit will be given only where the solution contains appropriate working.

3 Square-ruled paper is provided.

SCOTTISH QUALIFICATIONS AUTHORITY

FORMULAE LIST

The roots of $ax^2 + bx + c = 0$ are $x = \dfrac{-b \pm \sqrt{(b^2 - 4ac)}}{2a}$

Sine rule: $\dfrac{a}{\sin A} = \dfrac{b}{\sin B} = \dfrac{c}{\sin C}$

Cosine rule: $a^2 = b^2 + c^2 - 2bc \cos A$ or $\cos A = \dfrac{b^2 + c^2 - a^2}{2bc}$

Area of a triangle: $\text{Area} = \frac{1}{2}ab \sin C$

Volume of a sphere: $\text{Volume} = \frac{4}{3}\pi r^3$

Volume of a cone: $\text{Volume} = \frac{1}{3}\pi r^2 h$

Volume of a cylinder: $\text{Volume} = \pi r^2 h$

Standard deviation: $s = \sqrt{\dfrac{\sum(x - \bar{x})^2}{n-1}} = \sqrt{\dfrac{\sum x^2 - (\sum x)^2 / n}{n-1}}$, where n is the sample size.

ALL questions should be attempted.

Marks

1. Ian's annual salary is £28 400. His boss tells him that his salary will increase by 2·3% per annum.

   What will Ian's annual salary be after 3 years?

   Give your answer to the nearest pound.   **3**

2. The diagram below shows a sector of a circle, centre C.

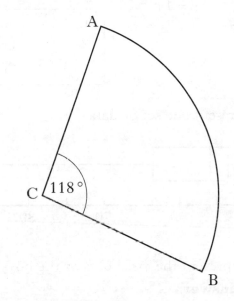

   The radius of the circle is 10·5 centimetres and angle ACB is 118°.

   Calculate the length of arc AB.   **3**

   [Turn over

Marks

3. This back-to-back stem and leaf diagram shows the results for a class in a recent mathematics examination.

```
        Girls    |   Boys
              1 | 3
              9 | 4 | 7  9
8  7  4  3  2 2 | 5 | 2  3  4  4  6  6  7  9
          9  4 | 6 | 3
        9  6  3 | 7 | 4  8
           8  1 | 8 | 7
```

n = 15   n = 14

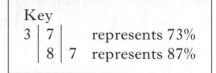

Key
3 | 7   represents 73%
  8 | 7 represents 87%

(*a*) A boxplot is drawn to represent one set of data.

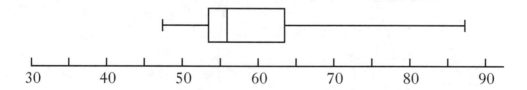

Does the boxplot above represent the girls' data or the boys' data?
Give a reason for your answer.   1

(*b*) For the **other** set of data, find:
  (i)   the median;   1
  (ii) the lower quartile;   1
  (iii) the upper quartile.   1

(*c*) Use the answers found in part (*b*) to construct a second boxplot.   2

(*d*) Make an appropriate comment about the distribution of data in the two sets.   1

Marks

4.

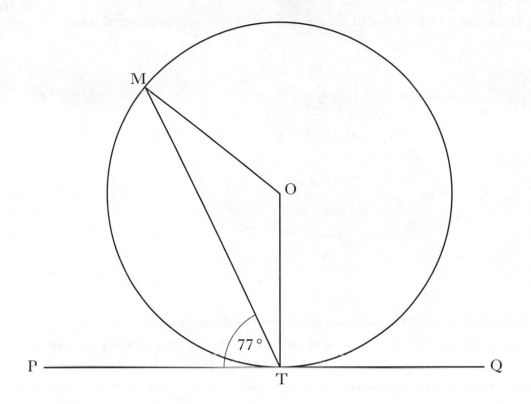

The tangent PQ touches the circle, centre O, at T.
Angle MTP is 77°.

(a) Calculate the size of angle MOT. **2**

(b) The radius of the circle is 8 centimetres.
Calculate the length of chord MT. **3**

[Turn over

Marks

5. A glass ornament in the shape of a cone is partly filled with coloured water.

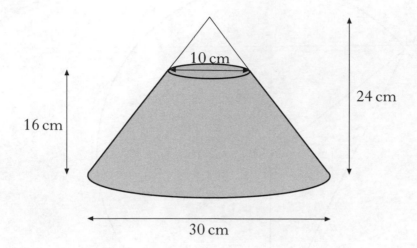

The cone is 24 centimetres high and has a base of diameter 30 centimetres.

The water is 16 centimetres deep and measures 10 centimetres across the top.

What is the volume of the water?

Give your answer correct to 2 significant figures.   **5**

6. Tasnim rolls a standard dice with faces numbered 1 to 6.

The probability that she gets a number less than 7 is

A   0

B $\frac{1}{7}$

C $\frac{1}{6}$

D   1.

Write down the letter that corresponds to the correct probability.   **1**

7. (a) Factorise **fully**

$$2x^2 - 18.$$ **2**

(b) Simplify

$$\frac{(2x+5)^2}{(2x-1)(2x+5)}.$$ **1**

Marks

8. Solve the equation

$$2x^2 - 6x - 5 = 0,$$

giving the roots correct to one decimal place.   **4**

9. The diagram shows two blocks of flats of equal height.

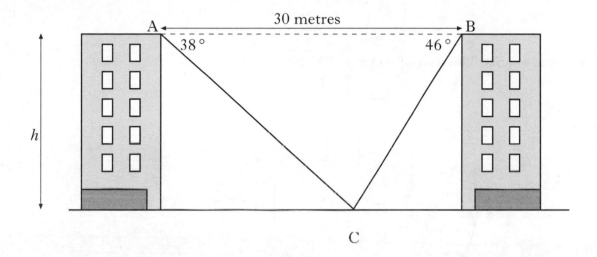

A and B represent points on the top of the flats and C represents a point on the ground between them.

To calculate the height, h, of each block of flats, a surveyor measures the angles of depression from A and B to C.

From A, the angle of depression is $38°$.
From B, the angle of depression is $46°$.
The distance AB is 30 metres.

Calculate the height, h, in metres.   **5**

10. Express $\dfrac{5p^2}{8} \div \dfrac{p}{2}$ as a fraction in its simplest form.   **3**

11. Change the subject of the formula

$$K = \frac{m^2 n}{p}$$

to m.   **3**

[Turn over for Questions 12, 13 and 14 on *Page eight*

Marks

12. Simplify the expression below, giving your answer with a positive power.

$$m^5 \times m^{-8}$$

2

13. Solve the equation

$$5 \tan x° - 6 = 2, \qquad 0 \le x < 360.$$

3

14. A mirror is shaped like part of a circle.

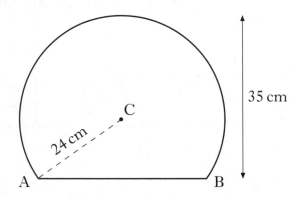

The radius of the circle, centre C, is 24 centimetres.
The height of the mirror is 35 centimetres.

Calculate the length of the base of the mirror, represented in the diagram by AB.

3

[END OF QUESTION PAPER]

2008

[BLANK PAGE]

X100/201

NATIONAL
QUALIFICATIONS
2008

TUESDAY, 20 MAY
1.00 PM – 1.45 PM

MATHEMATICS
INTERMEDIATE 2
Units 1, 2 and 3
Paper 1
(Non-calculator)

Read carefully

1   **You may <u>NOT</u> use a calculator.**

2   Full credit will be given only where the solution contains appropriate working.

3   Square-ruled paper is provided.

FORMULAE LIST

The roots of $ax^2 + bx + c = 0$ are $x = \dfrac{-b \pm \sqrt{(b^2 - 4ac)}}{2a}$

Sine rule: $\dfrac{a}{\sin A} = \dfrac{b}{\sin B} = \dfrac{c}{\sin C}$

Cosine rule: $a^2 = b^2 + c^2 - 2bc \cos A$ or $\cos A = \dfrac{b^2 + c^2 - a^2}{2bc}$

Area of a triangle: $\text{Area} = \frac{1}{2}ab \sin C$

Volume of a sphere: $\text{Volume} = \frac{4}{3}\pi r^3$

Volume of a cone: $\text{Volume} = \frac{1}{3}\pi r^2 h$

Volume of a cylinder: $\text{Volume} = \pi r^2 h$

Standard deviation: $s = \sqrt{\dfrac{\sum(x - \bar{x})^2}{n - 1}} = \sqrt{\dfrac{\sum x^2 - (\sum x)^2 / n}{n - 1}}$, where n is the sample size.

Marks

ALL questions should be attempted.

1. A straight line has equation $y = 4x + 5$.
   State the gradient of this line.   **1**

2. Multiply out the brackets and collect like terms.

   $$(3x + 2)(x - 5) + 8x$$ **3**

3. The stem and leaf diagram shows the number of points gained by the football teams in the Premiership League in a season.

   $$
   \begin{array}{c|cccccc}
   3 & 3 & 3 & 3 & 9 \\
   4 & 1 & 4 & 5 & 5 & 7 & 8 \\
   5 & 0 & 2 & 3 & 3 & 6 & 6 \\
   6 & 0 \\
   7 & 5 & 9 \\
   8 & \\
   9 & 0 \\
   \end{array}
   $$

   n = 20   4 | 1 represents 41 points

   (a) Arsenal finished 1st in the Premiership with 90 points.
       In what position did Southampton finish if they gained 47 points?   **1**

   (b) What is the probability that a team chosen at random scored less than 44 points?   **1**

4. (a) Factorise

   $$x^2 - y^2.$$ **1**

   (b) Hence, or otherwise, find the value of

   $$9{\cdot}3^2 - 0{\cdot}7^2.$$ **2**

   [Turn over

Marks

5. In a survey, the number of books carried by each girl in a group of students was recorded.

   The results are shown in the frequency table below.

Number of books	Frequency
0	1
1	2
2	3
3	5
4	5
5	6
6	2
7	1

   (a) Copy this frequency table and add a cumulative frequency column. **1**

   (b) For this data, find:
      (i)   the median; **1**
      (ii)   the lower quartile; **1**
      (iii)   the upper quartile. **1**

   (c) Calculate the semi-interquartile range. **1**

   (d) In the same survey, the number of books carried by each boy was also recorded.

   The semi-interquartile range was 0·75.

   Make an appropriate comment comparing the distribution of data for the girls and the boys. **1**

6. Triangle PQR is shown below.

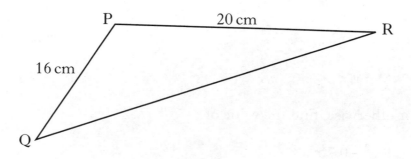

   If sin P = $\frac{1}{4}$, calculate the area of triangle PQR. **2**

Marks

7.

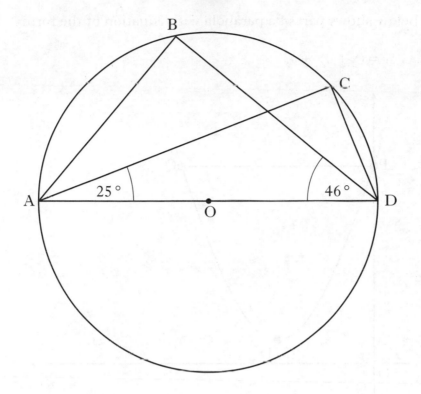

AD is a diameter of a circle, centre O.

B and C are points on the circumference of the circle.

Angle CAD = 25°.

Angle BDA = 46°.

Calculate the size of angle BAC.   3

8. Part of the graph of $y = a \sin bx°$ is shown in the diagram.

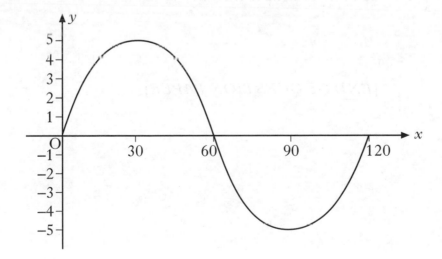

State the values of a and b.   2

[Turn over for Questions 9 and 10 on *Page six*

Marks

9. The graph below shows part of a parabola with equation of the form

$$y = (x + a)^2 + b.$$

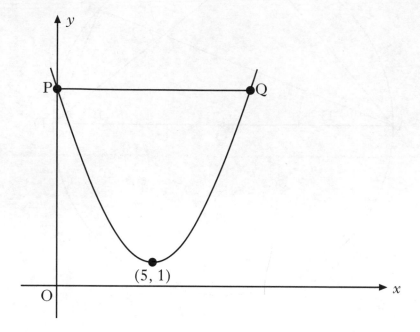

(5, 1)

(a) State the values of a and b. 2

(b) State the equation of the axis of symmetry of the parabola. 1

(c) The line PQ is parallel to the x-axis.
Find the coordinates of points P and Q. 3

10. If $\sin x° = \frac{4}{5}$ and $\cos x° = \frac{3}{5}$, calculate the value of $\tan x°$. 2

[END OF QUESTION PAPER]

X100/203

NATIONAL QUALIFICATIONS 2008	TUESDAY, 20 MAY 2.05 PM – 3.35 PM	**MATHEMATICS** INTERMEDIATE 2 Units 1, 2 and 3 Paper 2

Read carefully

1   **Calculators may be used in this paper.**

2   Full credit will be given only where the solution contains appropriate working.

3   Square-ruled paper is provided.

LI X100/203 6/24970

FORMULAE LIST

The roots of $ax^2 + bx + c = 0$ are $x = \dfrac{-b \pm \sqrt{(b^2 - 4ac)}}{2a}$

Sine rule: $\dfrac{a}{\sin A} = \dfrac{b}{\sin B} = \dfrac{c}{\sin C}$

Cosine rule: $a^2 = b^2 + c^2 - 2bc \cos A$ or $\cos A = \dfrac{b^2 + c^2 - a^2}{2bc}$

Area of a triangle: $\text{Area} = \tfrac{1}{2} ab \sin C$

Volume of a sphere: $\text{Volume} = \tfrac{4}{3} \pi r^3$

Volume of a cone: $\text{Volume} = \tfrac{1}{3} \pi r^2 h$

Volume of a cylinder: $\text{Volume} = \pi r^2 h$

Standard deviation: $s = \sqrt{\dfrac{\sum (x - \bar{x})^2}{n - 1}} = \sqrt{\dfrac{\sum x^2 - (\sum x)^2 / n}{n - 1}}$, where n is the sample size.

ALL questions should be attempted.

Marks

1. Calculate the **compound interest** earned when £50000 is invested for 4 years at 4·5% per annum.

   Give your answer to the nearest penny.

   4

2. Jim Reid keeps his washing in a basket. The basket is in the shape of a prism.

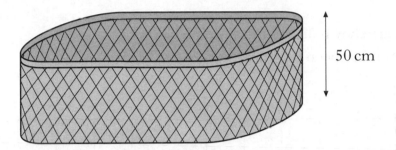

   The height of the basket is 50 centimetres.

   The cross section of the basket consists of a rectangle and two semi-circles with measurements as shown.

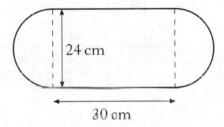

   (a) Find the volume of the basket in cubic centimetres.

   Give your answer correct to three significant figures.

   4

   Jim keeps his ironing in a storage box which has a volume **half** that of the basket.

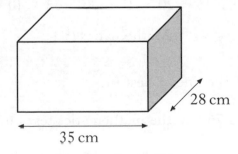

   The storage box is in the shape of a cuboid, 35 centimetres long and 28 centimetres broad.

   (b) Find the height of the storage box.

   3

Marks

3. The results for a group of students who sat tests in mathematics and physics are shown below.

Mathematics (%)	10	18	26	32	49
Physics (%)	25	35	30	40	41

(a) Calculate the standard deviation for the mathematics test.   **4**

(b) The standard deviation for physics was 6·8.

Make an appropriate comment on the distribution of marks in the two tests.   **1**

These marks are shown on the scattergraph below.
A line of best fit has been drawn.

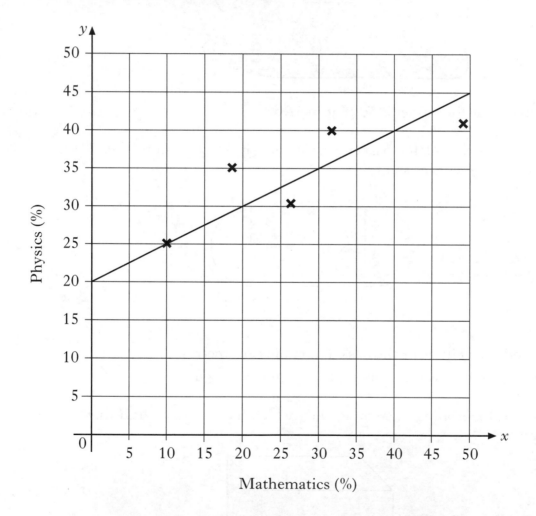

(c) Find the equation of the line of best fit.   **3**

(d) Another pupil scored 76% in the mathematics test but was absent from the physics test.

Use your answer to part (c) to predict his physics mark.   **1**

Marks

4. Suzie has a new mobile phone. She is charged x pence per minute for calls and y pence for each text she sends.   During the first month her calls last a total of 280 minutes and she sends 70 texts. Her bill is £52·50.

(a) Write down an equation in x and y which satisfies the above condition.   **1**

The next month she reduces her bill. She restricts her calls to 210 minutes and sends 40 texts. Her bill is £38·00.

(b) Write down a second equation in x and y which satisfies this condition.   **1**

(c) Calculate the price per minute for a call and the price for each text sent.   **4**

5. Triangle DEF is shown below.

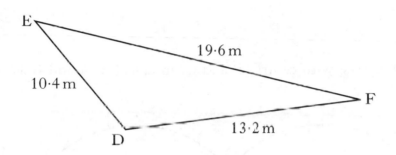

It has sides of length 10·4 metres, 13·2 metres and 19·6 metres.
Calculate the size of angle EDF.
Do not use a scale drawing.   **3**

6. Solve the equation

$$5x^2 + 4x - 2 = 0,$$

giving the roots correct to 2 decimal places.   **4**

[Turn over

Marks

7. (a) Simplify

$$\frac{m^5}{m^3}.$$

1

(b) Express

$$2\sqrt{5} + \sqrt{20} - \sqrt{45}$$

as a surd in its simplest form.

3

8. Solve the equation

$$4\cos x° + 3 = 0, \qquad 0 \leq x \leq 360.$$

3

9. Two identical circles, with centres P and Q, intersect at A and B as shown in the diagram.

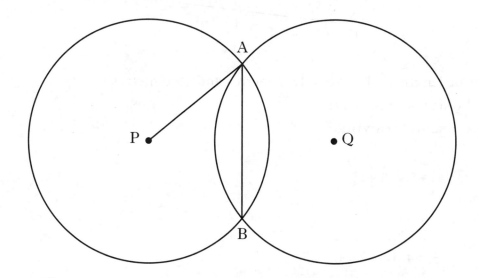

The radius of each circle is 10 centimetres.
The length of the common chord, AB, is 12 centimetres.

Calculate PQ, the distance between the centres of the two circles.

5

Marks

10. Change the subject of the formula

$$p = q + \sqrt{a}$$

to a.

2

11. Express

$$\frac{2}{a} - \frac{3}{(a+4)}, \qquad a \neq 0, \ a \neq -4,$$

as a single fraction in its simplest form.

3

[END OF QUESTION PAPER]

[BLANK PAGE]

2009

[BLANK PAGE]

X100/201

NATIONAL
QUALIFICATIONS
2009

THURSDAY, 21 MAY
1.00 PM – 1.45 PM

MATHEMATICS
INTERMEDIATE 2
Units 1, 2 and 3
Paper 1
(Non-calculator)

Read carefully

1   **You may <u>NOT</u> use a calculator.**

2   Full credit will be given only where the solution contains appropriate working.

3   Square-ruled paper is provided.

FORMULAE LIST

The roots of $ax^2 + bx + c = 0$ are $x = \dfrac{-b \pm \sqrt{(b^2 - 4ac)}}{2a}$

Sine rule: $\dfrac{a}{\sin A} = \dfrac{b}{\sin B} = \dfrac{c}{\sin C}$

Cosine rule: $a^2 = b^2 + c^2 - 2bc \cos A$ or $\cos A = \dfrac{b^2 + c^2 - a^2}{2bc}$

Area of a triangle: $\text{Area} = \frac{1}{2} ab \sin C$

Volume of a sphere: $\text{Volume} = \frac{4}{3} \pi r^3$

Volume of a cone: $\text{Volume} = \frac{1}{3} \pi r^2 h$

Volume of a cylinder: $\text{Volume} = \pi r^2 h$

Standard deviation: $s = \sqrt{\dfrac{\sum (x - \bar{x})^2}{n - 1}} = \sqrt{\dfrac{\sum x^2 - (\sum x)^2 / n}{n - 1}}$, where n is the sample size.

Marks

ALL questions should be attempted.

1. The number of goals scored one weekend by each team in the Football League is shown below.

    0   1   1   2   1   0   0   5   0   1   3

    0   2   2   1   1   3   0   0   2   4   1

    (a) Construct a dotplot for the data.   2

    (b) The shape of the distribution is

                A   skewed to the right
                B   symmetric
                C   skewed to the left
                D   uniform.

        Write down the letter that corresponds to the correct shape.   1

2.

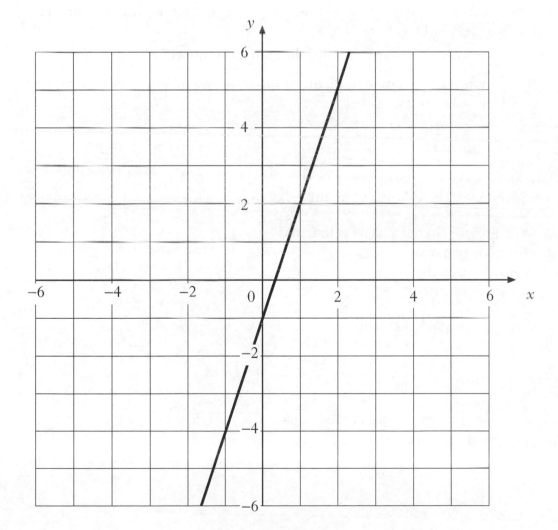

    Find the equation of the straight line shown in the diagram.   3

Marks

3. Factorise

$$x^2 - 5x - 24.$$

2

4. Multiply out the brackets and collect like terms.

$$(x + 5)(2x^2 - 3x - 1)$$

3

5. (*a*) The marks of a group of students in their October test are listed below.

41   56   68   59   43   37   70   58   61   47   75   66

Calculate:

(i)   the median;   1

(ii)   the semi-interquartile range.   3

(*b*) The teacher arranges extra homework classes for the students before the next test in December.

In this test, the median is 67 and the semi-interquartile range is 7.

Make **two** appropriate comments comparing the marks in the October and December tests.

2

6. An angle, $a°$, can be described by the following statements.

- a is greater than 0 and less than 360
- $\sin a°$ is negative
- $\cos a°$ is positive
- $\tan a°$ is negative

Write down a possible value for a.

1

7. A straight line is represented by the equation $x + y = 5$.
Find the gradient of this line.

2

Marks

8. Sketch the graph of $y = 4\cos 2x°$, $0 \le x \le 360$.   **3**

9. The diagram below shows part of a parabola with equation of the form

$$y = (x + a)^2 + b.$$

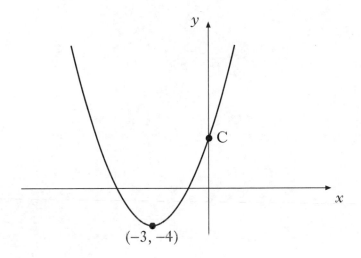

(−3, −4)

(*a*) Write down the equation of the axis of symmetry of the graph.   **1**

(*b*) Write down the equation of the parabola.   **2**

(*c*) Find the coordinates of C.   **2**

10. Simplify

$$\frac{\cos^3 x°}{1 - \sin^2 x°}.$$ **2**

[*END OF QUESTION PAPER*]

[BLANK PAGE]

X100/203

NATIONAL
QUALIFICATIONS
2009

THURSDAY, 21 MAY
2.05 PM – 3.35 PM

MATHEMATICS
INTERMEDIATE 2
Units 1, 2 and 3
Paper 2

Read carefully

1 **Calculators may be used in this paper.**

2 Full credit will be given only where the solution contains appropriate working.

3 Square-ruled paper is provided.

FORMULAE LIST

The roots of $ax^2 + bx + c = 0$ are $x = \dfrac{-b \pm \sqrt{(b^2 - 4ac)}}{2a}$

Sine rule: $\dfrac{a}{\sin A} = \dfrac{b}{\sin B} = \dfrac{c}{\sin C}$

Cosine rule: $a^2 = b^2 + c^2 - 2bc \cos A$ or $\cos A = \dfrac{b^2 + c^2 - a^2}{2bc}$

Area of a triangle: $\text{Area} = \frac{1}{2} ab \sin C$

Volume of a sphere: $\text{Volume} = \frac{4}{3} \pi r^3$

Volume of a cone: $\text{Volume} = \frac{1}{3} \pi r^2 h$

Volume of a cylinder: $\text{Volume} = \pi r^2 h$

Standard deviation: $s = \sqrt{\dfrac{\sum (x - \bar{x})^2}{n - 1}} = \sqrt{\dfrac{\sum x^2 - (\sum x)^2 / n}{n - 1}}$, where n is the sample size.

ALL questions should be attempted.

Marks

1. A new book "Intermediate 2 Maths is Fun" was published in 2006.
    There were 3000 sales of the book during that year.
    Sales rose by 11% in 2007 then fell by 10% in 2008.

    Were the sales in 2008 more or less than the sales in 2006?

    You must give a reason for your answer.   3

2. The heights, in centimetres, of seven netball players are given below.

    173   176   168   166   170   180   171

    For this sample, calculate:

    (*a*) the mean;   1

    (*b*) the standard deviation.   3

    Show clearly all your working.

    [Turn over

Marks

3.   A company manufactures aluminium tubes.

The cross-section of one of the tubes is shown in the diagram below.

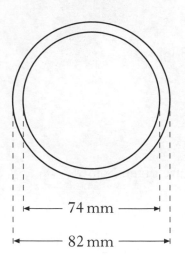
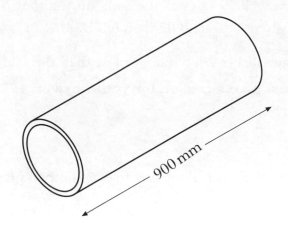

74 mm

82 mm

900 mm

The inner diameter is 74 millimetres.

The outer diameter is 82 millimetres.

The tube is 900 millimetres long.

Calculate the volume of aluminium used to make the tube.

Give your answer correct to three significant figures.   **5**

4.   There are 14 cars and 60 passengers on the morning crossing of the ferry from Wemyss Bay to Rothesay. The total takings are £344·30.

(*a*) Let x pounds be the cost for a car and y pounds be the cost for a passenger.

Write down an equation in x and y which satisfies the above condition.   **1**

(*b*) There are 21 cars and 40 passengers on the evening crossing of the ferry. The total takings are £368·95.

Write down a second equation in x and y which satisfies this condition.   **1**

(*c*) Find the cost for a car and the cost for a passenger on the ferry.   **4**

Marks

5. A pet shop manufactures protective dog collars.

   In the diagram below the shaded area represents one of these collars.

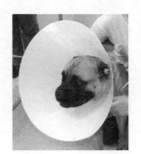

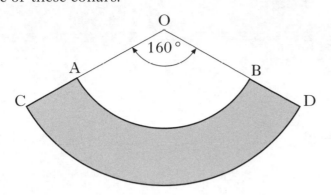

   AB and CD are arcs of the circles with centres at O.

   The radius, OA, is 10 inches and the radius, OC, is 18 inches.

   Angle AOB is 160°.

   Calculate the area of a collar.

   4

6. The Bermuda triangle is an area in the Atlantic Ocean where many planes and ships have mysteriously disappeared.

   Its vertices are at Bermuda (B), Miami (M) and Puerto Rico (P).

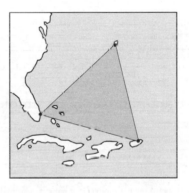

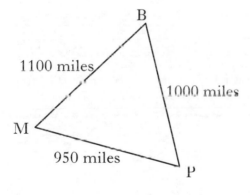

   Calculate the size of angle BPM.

   3

7. Solve the equation

$$x^2 + 5x + 3 = 0,$$

   giving the roots correct to one decimal place.

   4

[Turn over

Marks

8. Express

$$\frac{2}{x-1} + \frac{4}{x+2} \qquad x \neq 1, \ x \neq -2$$

as a single fraction in its simplest form.

3

9. Change the subject of the formula

$$A = \frac{1}{2}h(a+b)$$

to h.

2

10. Solve the equation

$$7\sin x° + 1 = -5, \qquad 0 \leq x \leq 360.$$

3

11. Express $\dfrac{12}{\sqrt{2}}$ with a rational denominator.

Give your answer in its simplest form.

2

12. Simplify $\dfrac{ab^6}{a^3b^2}$.

2

Marks

13. For reasons of safety, a building is supported by two wooden struts, represented by DB and DC in the diagram below.

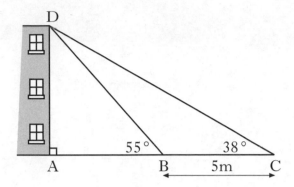

Angle ABD = 55°.

Angle BCD = 38°.

BC is 5 metres.

Calculate the height of the building represented by AD.

5

14. A railway goes through an underground tunnel.

The diagram below shows the cross-section of the tunnel. It consists of part of a circle with a horizontal base.

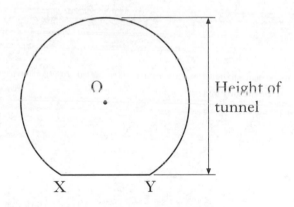

Height of tunnel

- The centre of the circle is O.
- XY is a chord of the circle.
- XY is 1·8 metres.
- The radius of the circle is 1·7 metres.

Find the height of the tunnel.

4

[END OF QUESTION PAPER]

[BLANK PAGE]

[BLANK PAGE]

X100/201

NATIONAL
QUALIFICATIONS
2010

FRIDAY, 21 MAY
1.00 PM – 1.45 PM

**MATHEMATICS
INTERMEDIATE 2**
Units 1, 2 and 3
Paper 1
(Non-calculator)

Read carefully

1   **You may NOT use a calculator.**

2   Full credit will be given only where the solution contains appropriate working.

3   Square-ruled paper is provided.

FORMULAE LIST

The roots of $ax^2 + bx + c = 0$ are $x = \dfrac{-b \pm \sqrt{(b^2 - 4ac)}}{2a}$

Sine rule: $\dfrac{a}{\sin A} = \dfrac{b}{\sin B} = \dfrac{c}{\sin C}$

Cosine rule: $a^2 = b^2 + c^2 - 2bc \cos A$ or $\cos A = \dfrac{b^2 + c^2 - a^2}{2bc}$

Area of a triangle: $\text{Area} = \frac{1}{2}ab \sin C$

Volume of a sphere: $\text{Volume} = \frac{4}{3}\pi r^3$

Volume of a cone: $\text{Volume} = \frac{1}{3}\pi r^2 h$

Volume of a cylinder: $\text{Volume} = \pi r^2 h$

Standard deviation: $s = \sqrt{\dfrac{\sum(x - \bar{x})^2}{n-1}} = \sqrt{\dfrac{\sum x^2 - (\sum x)^2 / n}{n-1}}$, where n is the sample size.

Marks

ALL questions should be attempted.

1.

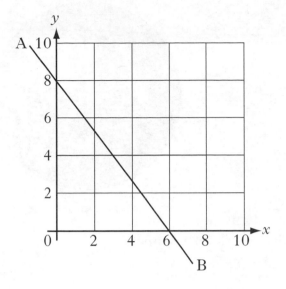

Find the equation of the straight line AB shown in the diagram.   3

2. The pupils in a primary class record their shoe sizes as shown below.

$$
\begin{array}{ccccc}
8 & 7 & 6 & 5 & 6 \\
5 & 7 & 11 & 7 & 7 \\
7 & 8 & 7 & 9 & 6 \\
8 & 6 & 5 & 9 & 7 \\
\end{array}
$$

(a) Construct a frequency table from the above data and add a cumulative frequency column.   2

(b) For this data, find:

   (i)   the median;   1

   (ii) the lower quartile;   1

   (iii) the upper quartile.   1

(c) Construct a boxplot for this data.   2

[Turn over

Marks

3. The diagram below represents a sphere.

6 cm

The sphere has a diameter of 6 centimetres.

Calculate its volume.

Take π = 3·14.   2

4. (*a*) Factorise

$$x^2 + x - 6.$$ 2

(*b*) Multiply out the brackets and collect like terms.

$$(3x + 2)(x^2 + 5x - 1)$$ 3

Marks

5. The diagram below shows the graph of $y = -x^2$.

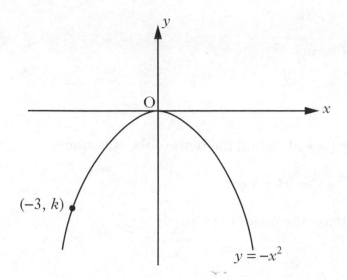

The point $(-3, k)$ lies on the graph.

Find the value of k.   **1**

6.

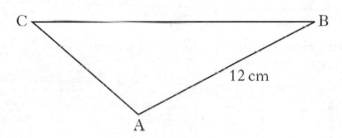

In triangle ABC, AB = 12 centimetres, $\sin C = \frac{1}{2}$ and $\sin B = \frac{1}{3}$.

Find the length of side AC.   **3**

[Turn over

Marks

7. Express

$$p^3(p^2 - p^{-3})$$

in its simplest form.   **2**

8. Maria has been asked to find the roots of the equation

$$x^2 + 3x + 5 = 0.$$

She decides to use the quadratic formula

$$x = \frac{-b \pm \sqrt{(b^2 - 4ac)}}{2a}.$$

(a) Calculate the value of $b^2 - 4ac$.   **1**

(b) Now explain why Maria cannot find the roots.   **1**

9. The graph shown below has an equation of the form $y = \cos(x - a)°$.

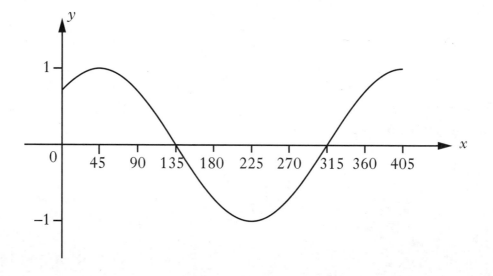

Write down the value of a.   **1**

Marks

10. The graph below shows part of a parabola with equation of the form $y = (x + a)^2 + b$.

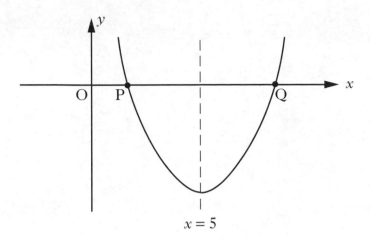

$x = 5$

The equation of the axis of symmetry of the parabola is $x = 5$.

(*a*) State the value of *a*.   **1**

(*b*) P is the point (2, 0). State the coordinates of Q.   **1**

(*c*) Calculate the value of *b*.   **2**

[END OF QUESTION PAPER]

[BLANK PAGE]

X100/203

NATIONAL
QUALIFICATIONS
2010

FRIDAY, 21 MAY
2.05 PM – 3.35 PM

MATHEMATICS
INTERMEDIATE 2
Units 1, 2 and 3
Paper 2

Read carefully

1 **Calculators may be used in this paper.**

2 Full credit will be given only where the solution contains appropriate working.

3 Square-ruled paper is provided.

FORMULAE LIST

The roots of $ax^2 + bx + c = 0$ are $x = \dfrac{-b \pm \sqrt{(b^2 - 4ac)}}{2a}$

Sine rule: $\dfrac{a}{\sin A} = \dfrac{b}{\sin B} = \dfrac{c}{\sin C}$

Cosine rule: $a^2 = b^2 + c^2 - 2bc \cos A$ or $\cos A = \dfrac{b^2 + c^2 - a^2}{2bc}$

Area of a triangle: $\text{Area} = \frac{1}{2} ab \sin C$

Volume of a sphere: $\text{Volume} = \frac{4}{3} \pi r^3$

Volume of a cone: $\text{Volume} = \frac{1}{3} \pi r^2 h$

Volume of a cylinder: $\text{Volume} = \pi r^2 h$

Standard deviation: $s = \sqrt{\dfrac{\sum (x - \bar{x})^2}{n - 1}} = \sqrt{\dfrac{\sum x^2 - (\sum x)^2 / n}{n - 1}}$, where n is the sample size.

Marks

ALL questions should be attempted.

1. An industrial machine costs £176 500.

   Its value depreciates by 4·25% each year.

   How much is it worth after 3 years?

   Give your answer correct to **three** significant figures.   **4**

2. Paul conducts a survey to find the most popular school lunch.

   - 30 pupils vote for Pasta
   - 40 pupils vote for Baked Potato
   - 2 pupils vote for Salad

   Paul wishes to draw a pie chart to illustrate his data. How many degrees must he use for each sector in his pie chart?

   Do not draw the pie chart.   **2**

3. The scattergraph shows the taxi fare, p pounds, plotted against the distance travelled, m miles. A line of best fit has been drawn.

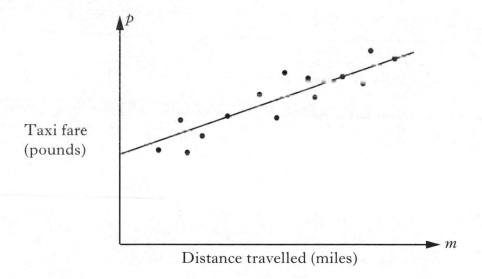

Distance travelled (miles)

The equation of the line of best fit is $p = 2 + 1·5\,m$.

Use this equation to predict the taxi fare for a journey of 6 miles.   **1**

[Turn over

Marks

4. A rugby team scored the following points in a series of matches.

$$13 \quad 7 \quad 0 \quad 9 \quad 7 \quad 8 \quad 5$$

(a) For this sample, calculate:

  (i) the mean;   **1**

  (ii) the standard deviation.   **3**

Show clearly all your working.

The following season, the team appoints a new coach.

A similar series of matches produces a mean of 27 and a standard deviation of $3 \cdot 25$.

(b) Make two valid comparisons about the performance of the team under the new coach.   **2**

5. Solve algebraically the system of equations

$$2x - 5y = 24$$
$$7x + 8y = 33.$$

  3

6. Express

$$\frac{s^2}{t} \times \frac{3t}{2s}$$

as a fraction in its simplest form.   **2**

7. Change the subject of the formula

$$P = 2(L + B)$$

to L.   **2**

Marks

8. Express

$$\sqrt{63} + \sqrt{28} - \sqrt{7}$$

as a surd in its simplest form.   **3**

9. The ends of a magazine rack are identical.

Each end is a sector of a circle with radius 14 centimetres.
The angle in each sector is $65°$.

The sectors are joined by two rectangles, each with length 40 centimetres.

The exterior is covered by material.
What area of material is required?   **4**

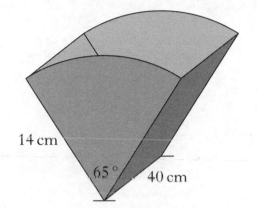

14 cm $65°$ 40 cm

10. The diagram below represents a rectangular garden with length $(x + 7)$ metres and breadth $(x + 3)$ metres.

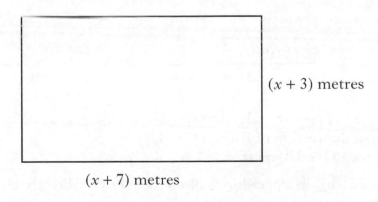

$(x + 3)$ metres

$(x + 7)$ metres

(a) Show that the area, A square metres, of the garden is given by

$$A = x^2 + 10x + 21.$$ **2**

(b) The area of the garden is 45 square metres. Find x.

Show clearly all your working.   **4**

Marks

11. A cylindrical container has a volume of 3260 cubic centimetres.

    The radius of the cross section is 6·4 centimetres.

    Calculate the height of the cylinder.

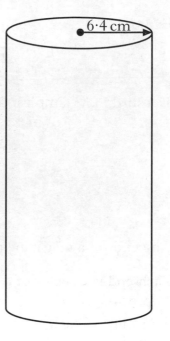

3

12. Two ships have located a wreck on the sea bed.

    In the diagram below, the points P and Q represent the two ships and the point R represents the wreck.

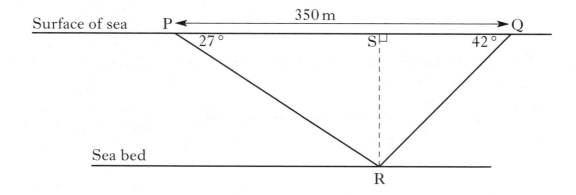

    The angle of depression of R from P is 27°.
    The angle of depression of R from Q is 42°.
    The distance PQ is 350 metres.

    Calculate QS, the distance ship Q has to travel to be directly above the wreck.

    Do not use a scale drawing.

5

Marks

13. Ocean World has an underwater viewing tunnel.

The diagram below shows the cross-section of the tunnel. It consists of part of a circle with a horizontal base.

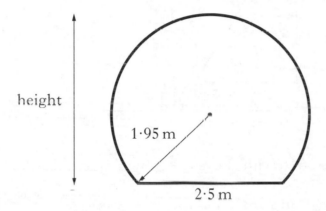

height

1·95 m

2·5 m

The radius of the circle is 1·95 metres and the width of the base is 2·5 metres.

Calculate the height of the tunnel.

4

[Turn over for Question 14 on *Page eight*

Marks

14. A surveyor views a lift as it travels up the outside of a building.

In the diagram below, the point L represents the lift.

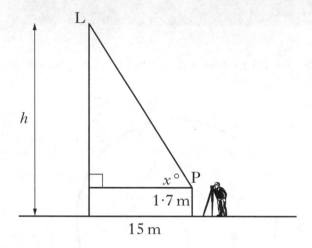

The height, *h* metres, of the lift above the ground is given by the formula

$$h = 15 \tan x° + 1·7,$$

where *x*° is the angle of elevation of the lift from the surveyor at point P.

(*a*) What is the height of the lift above the ground when the angle of elevation from P is 25°?

2

(*b*) What is the angle of elevation at point P when the height of the lift above the ground is 18·4 metres?

3

[*END OF QUESTION PAPER*]

[BLANK PAGE]

X100/201

NATIONAL QUALIFICATIONS 2011	WEDNESDAY, 18 MAY 1.00 PM – 1.45 PM	**MATHEMATICS** INTERMEDIATE 2 Units 1, 2 and 3 Paper 1 (Non-calculator)

Read carefully

1 **You may <u>NOT</u> use a calculator.**

2 Full credit will be given only where the solution contains appropriate working.

3 Square-ruled paper is provided. If you make use of this, you should write your name on it clearly and put it inside your answer booklet.

FORMULAE LIST

The roots of $ax^2 + bx + c = 0$ are $x = \dfrac{-b \pm \sqrt{(b^2 - 4ac)}}{2a}$

Sine rule: $\dfrac{a}{\sin A} = \dfrac{b}{\sin B} = \dfrac{c}{\sin C}$

Cosine rule: $a^2 = b^2 + c^2 - 2bc \cos A$ or $\cos A = \dfrac{b^2 + c^2 - a^2}{2bc}$

Area of a triangle: $\text{Area} = \frac{1}{2} ab \sin C$

Volume of a sphere: $\text{Volume} = \frac{4}{3} \pi r^3$

Volume of a cone: $\text{Volume} = \frac{1}{3} \pi r^2 h$

Volume of a cylinder: $\text{Volume} = \pi r^2 h$

Standard deviation: $s = \sqrt{\dfrac{\sum (x - \bar{x})^2}{n - 1}} = \sqrt{\dfrac{\sum x^2 - (\sum x)^2 / n}{n - 1}}$, where n is the sample size.

Marks

ALL questions should be attempted.

1. Sandi takes the bus to work each day.

    Over a two week period, she records the number of minutes the bus is late each day. The results are shown below.

    $$5 \quad 6 \quad 15 \quad 0 \quad 6 \quad 11 \quad 2 \quad 9 \quad 8 \quad 7$$

    (*a*) From the above data, find:

       (i) the median;   1

      (ii) the lower quartile;   1

    (iii) the upper quartile.   1

    (*b*) Construct a boxplot for the data.   2

    Sandi decides to take the train over the next two week period and records the number of minutes the train is late each day.

    The boxplot, drawn below, was constructed for the new data.

    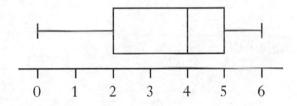

    (*c*) Compare the two boxplots and comment.   1

2. Multiply out the brackets and collect like terms.

    $$5x + (3x + 2)(2x - 7)$$

                                                               3

[Turn over

Marks

3. A circle, centre O, is shown below.

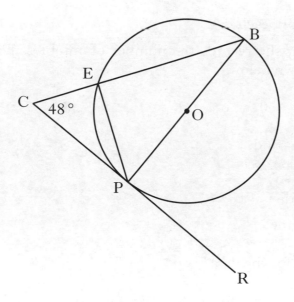

In the circle

- PB is a diameter
- CR is a tangent to the circle at point P
- Angle BCP is 48°.

Calculate the size of angle EPR.   **3**

4. Three of the following have the same value.

$$2\sqrt{6}, \qquad \sqrt{2} \times \sqrt{12}, \qquad 3\sqrt{8}, \qquad \sqrt{24}.$$

Which one has a different value?

You must give a reason for your answer.   **2**

Marks

5.

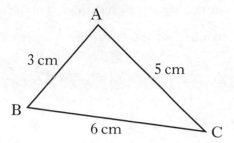

In triangle ABC, show that $\cos B = \dfrac{5}{9}$.

3

6. Evaluate

$$9^{\frac{3}{2}}.$$

2

7. Part of the graph of $y = a\cos bx°$ is shown in the diagram.

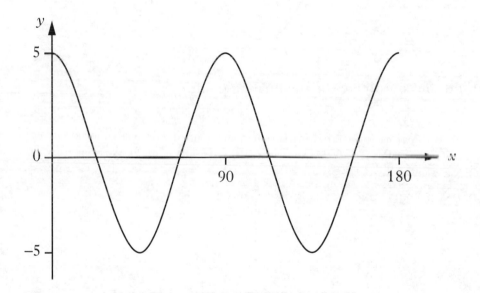

State the values of a and b.

2

[Turn over

Marks

8. A straight line is represented by the equation $y = mx + c$.

Sketch a possible straight line graph to illustrate this equation when $m > 0$ and $c < 0$.   **2**

9. (a) Factorise $x^2 - 4x - 21$.   **2**

(b) Hence write down the roots of the equation

$$x^2 - 4x - 21 = 0.$$ **1**

(c) The graph of $y = x^2 - 4x - 21$ is shown in the diagram.

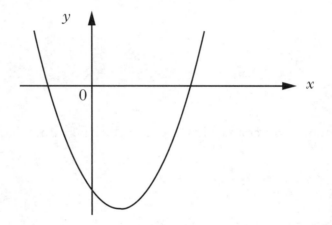

Find the coordinates of the turning point.   **3**

10.

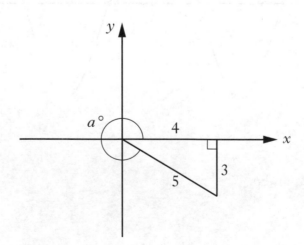

Write down the value of $\cos a°$.   **1**

[*END OF QUESTION PAPER*]

X100/203

NATIONAL QUALIFICATIONS 2011	WEDNESDAY, 18 MAY 2.05 PM – 3.35 PM	MATHEMATICS INTERMEDIATE 2 Units 1, 2 and 3 Paper 2

Read carefully

1 **Calculators may be used in this paper.**

2 Full credit will be given only where the solution contains appropriate working.

3 Square-ruled paper is provided. If you make use of this, you should write your name on it clearly and put it inside your answer booklet.

FORMULAE LIST

The roots of $ax^2 + bx + c = 0$ are $x = \dfrac{-b \pm \sqrt{(b^2 - 4ac)}}{2a}$

Sine rule: $\dfrac{a}{\sin A} = \dfrac{b}{\sin B} = \dfrac{c}{\sin C}$

Cosine rule: $a^2 = b^2 + c^2 - 2bc \cos A$ or $\cos A = \dfrac{b^2 + c^2 - a^2}{2bc}$

Area of a triangle: $\text{Area} = \frac{1}{2}ab \sin C$

Volume of a sphere: $\text{Volume} = \frac{4}{3}\pi r^3$

Volume of a cone: $\text{Volume} = \frac{1}{3}\pi r^2 h$

Volume of a cylinder: $\text{Volume} = \pi r^2 h$

Standard deviation: $s = \sqrt{\dfrac{\sum(x - \bar{x})^2}{n-1}} = \sqrt{\dfrac{\sum x^2 - (\sum x)^2 / n}{n-1}}$, where n is the sample size.

Marks

ALL questions should be attempted.

1.

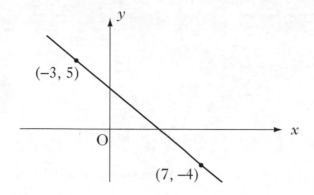

Calculate the gradient of the straight line passing through the points $(-3, 5)$ and $(7, -4)$.

1

2. It is estimated that house prices will increase at the rate of $3 \cdot 15\%$ per annum.

A house is valued at £134 750. If its value increases at the predicted rate, calculate its value after 3 years.

Give your answer correct to **four** significant figures.

4

3. Change the subject of the formula

$$A = 4\pi r^2$$

to r.

2

[Turn over

Marks

4. The Battle of Largs in 1263 is commemorated by a monument known as The Pencil.

This monument is in the shape of a cylinder with a cone on top.

The cylinder part has diameter 3 metres and height 15 metres.

(*a*) Calculate the volume of the **cylinder** part of The Pencil.   **2**

The volume of the **cone** part of The Pencil is 5·7 cubic metres.

(*b*) Calculate the **total** height of The Pencil.   **3**

5. The diagram below shows a sector of a circle, centre C.

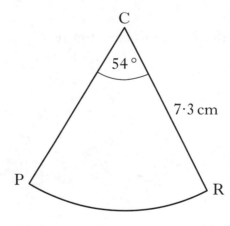

The radius of the circle is 7·3 centimetres and angle PCR is 54°.

Calculate the area of the sector PCR.   **3**

Marks

6. A sample of six boxes contains the following numbers of pins per box.

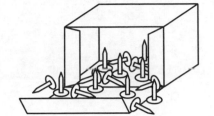

43   39   41   40   39   44

(a) For the above data, calculate:

   (i) the mean;   **1**

   (ii) the standard deviation.   **3**

The company which produces the pins claims that "the mean number of pins per box is 40 ± 2 and the standard deviation is less than 3".

(b) Does the data in part (a) support the claim made by the company?

   Give reasons for your answer.   **2**

7. Alan is taking part in a quiz. He is awarded x points for each correct answer and y points for each wrong answer. During the quiz, Alan gets 24 questions correct and 6 wrong. He scores 60 points.

(a) Write down an equation in x and y which satisfies the above condition.   **1**

Helen also takes part in the quiz. She gets 20 questions correct and 10 wrong. She scores 40 points.

(b) Write down a second equation in x and y which satisfies this condition.   **1**

(c) Calculate the score for David who gets 17 correct and 13 wrong.   **4**

8. Simplify

$$\frac{3x-15}{(x-5)^2}.$$ **2**

9. Express

$$\frac{3}{x} - \frac{4}{x+1}, \qquad x \neq 0, \ x \neq -1$$

as a single fraction in its simplest form.   **3**

Marks

10. Solve the equation

$$2 \tan x° - 3 = 5, \qquad 0 \leq x \leq 360.$$

3

11. Solve the equation

$$4x^2 - 7x + 1 = 0,$$

giving the roots correct to 1 decimal place.

4

12.

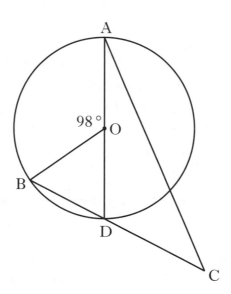

AD is a diameter of a circle, centre O.
B is a point on the circumference of the circle.
The chord BD is extended to a point C, outside the circle.
Angle BOA = 98°.
DC = 9 centimetres. The radius of the circle is 7 centimetres.

Calculate the length of AC.

5

Marks

13. A circular saw can be adjusted to change the depth of blade that is exposed below the horizontal guide.

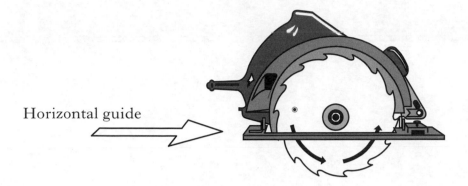

Horizontal guide

The circle, centre O, below represents the blade and the line AB represents part of the horizontal guide.

This blade has a radius of 110 millimetres.

If AB has length 140 millimetres, calculate the depth, *d* millimetres, of saw exposed.

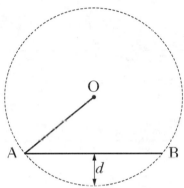

4

14. Prove that
$$\frac{\sin^2 A}{1 - \sin^2 A} = \tan^2 A.$$

2

[END OF QUESTION PAPER]

[BLANK PAGE]

SQA INTERMEDIATE 2
MATHEMATICS: UNITS 1, 2 and 3 2007–2011

MATHEMATICS INTERMEDIATE 2
UNITS 1, 2 AND 3 PAPER 1
(NON-CALCULATOR)
2007

1. 29/100 (or equivalent)

2. $y = 4x - 3$

3. 314 cubic cm

4. $(3, -4)$

5. $x^3 + 7x^2 - 36$

6. (a) Proof

   By finding $\bar{x} = 2$ and $(x - \bar{x})^2 = 1, 1, 1, 0, 9$

   substitute into formula $\sqrt{\dfrac{12}{5-1}}$

   leading to $\sqrt{3}$

   (b) $\sqrt{3}$

7. (a) $x = 0, x = 8$

   (b) $x = 4$

   (c) $(4, 16)$

8. -0.5

9. $5\sqrt{2}$

10. (a) $a = 4$

    (b) $b = 2$

11.

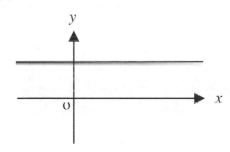

MATHEMATICS INTERMEDIATE 2
UNITS 1, 2 AND 3 PAPER 2
2007

1. £30 405

2. 21·6 cm

3. (a) Boys' data, with valid reason

   (b) (i) 58

       (ii) 52

       (iii) 76

   (c)

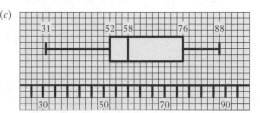

   (d) The girls' results are more widely spread than the boys'

4. (a) 154°

   (b) 15·6 cm

5. 5400 cubic centimetres

6. D

7. (a) $2(x + 3)(x - 3)$

   (b) $\dfrac{2x + 5}{2x - 1}$

8. $x = -0.7, x = 3.7$

9. 13·4 metres

10. $\dfrac{5p}{4}$

11. $m = \sqrt{\dfrac{kp}{n}}$

12. $1/m^3$

13. $x = 58$ and 238

14. 42·7 cm

MATHEMATICS INTERMEDIATE 2
UNITS 1, 2 AND 3 PAPER 1
(NON-CALCULATOR)
2008

1. gradient is 4

2. $3x^2 - 5x - 10$

3. (a) 12th

   (b) $\frac{5}{20}$ or equivalent

4. (a) $(x + y)(x - y)$

   (b) 86

5. (a)

Number of books	Frequency	Cumulative Frequency
0	1	1
1	2	3
2	3	6
3	5	11
4	5	16
5	6	22
6	2	24
7	1	25

   (b) $Q_2 = 4$, $Q_1 = 2.5$ $Q_3 = 5$

   (c) 1·25

   (d) number of textbooks more spread out for girls

6. 40 sq cm

7. 19°

8. $a = 5$, $b = 3$

9. (a) $a = -5$, $b = 1$

   (b) $x = 5$

   (c) P(0, 26), Q(10, 26)

10. $\frac{4}{3}$

MATHEMATICS INTERMEDIATE 2
UNITS 1, 2 AND 3 PAPER 2
2008

1. £9625·93

2. (a) 58 600 cubic cm

   (b) 29·9 cm

3. (a) 14·8

   (b) The physics marks were more consistent than the maths marks (since 6·8 < 14·8)

   (c) $y = \frac{1}{2}x + 20$

   (d) 58%

4. (a) $280x + 70y = 5250$

   (b) $210x + 40y = 3800$

   (c) Calls cost 16 pence per minute, texts cost 11 pence each

5. Angle EDF = 111·8°

6. 0·35, −1·15

7. (a) m^2

   (b) $\sqrt{5}$

8. $x = 138·6, 221·4$

9. 16 cm

10. $a = (p - q)^2$

11. $\dfrac{8 - a}{a(a + 4)}$

MATHEMATICS INTERMEDIATE 2 UNITS 1, 2 AND 3 PAPER 1 (NON-CALCULATOR) 2009

1. (a)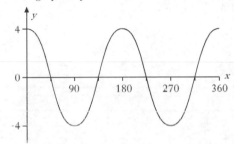

   (b) A

2. $y = 3x - 1$

3. $(x - 8)(x + 3)$

4. $2x^3 + 7x^2 - 16x - 5$

5. (a) (i) 58·5 (ii) 11

   (b) In December, the marks (on average) are better and less spread out

6. Any value for a such that $270 < a < 360$

7. -1

8. The graph of $y = 4\cos 2x°$ drawn from $0°$ to $360°$

9. (a) $x = -3$

   (b) $y = (x + 3)^2 - 4$

   (c) (0,5)

10. $\cos x°$

MATHEMATICS INTERMEDIATE 2 UNITS 1, 2 AND 3 PAPER 2 2009

1. There were 3 sales fewer in 2008 or There were fewer sales in 2008 because $2997 < 3000$

2. (a) 172 cm

   (b) 4·8 cm

3. 882 000 mm³

4. (a) $14x + 60y = 344·30$

   (b) $21x + 40y = 368·95$

   (c) A car costs £11·95 and a passenger £2·95

5. 313 square inches

6. 68·6°

7. $x = -0·7$, $x = -4·3$

8. $\dfrac{6x}{(x - 1)(x + 2)}$

9. $h = \dfrac{2A}{(a + b)}$

10. $x = 239$ and $x = 301$

11. $6\sqrt{2}$

12. $a^{-2}b^4$ or $\dfrac{b^4}{a^2}$

13. 8·6 metres

14. 3·14 metres

MATHEMATICS INTERMEDIATE 2 UNITS 1, 2 AND 3 PAPER 1 (NON-CALCULATOR) 2010

1. $y = -\dfrac{4}{3}x + 8$

2. (*a*)

Shoe size	frequency	cumulative frequency
5	3	3
6	4	7
7	7	14
8	3	17
9	2	19
10	0	19
11	1	20

(*b*) (i) 7   (ii) 6   (iii) 8

(*c*)

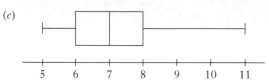

3. 113·04 cubic centimetres

4. (*a*) $(x + 3)(x - 2)$

(*b*) $3x^3 + 17x^2 + 7x - 2$

5. -9

6. 8 centimetres

7. $p^5 - 1$

8. (*a*) -11

(*b*) The square root of a negative number does not exist

9. 45

10. (*a*) -5

(*b*) $(8, 0)$

(*c*) -9

MATHEMATICS INTERMEDIATE 2 UNITS 1, 2 AND 3 PAPER 2 2010

1. £155 000

2. 150°, 200°, 10°

3. £11

4. (*a*) (i) 7   (ii) 3·958

(*b*) The team scores more points under the new coach. The team is more consistent.

5. $x = 7$, $y = -2$

6. $\dfrac{3s}{2}$

7. $L = \dfrac{P}{2} - B$ or $L = \dfrac{P - 2B}{2}$

8. $4\sqrt{7}$

9. 1342·35 square centimetres

10. (*a*) Proof
$(x + 7)(x + 3)$
evidence of four correct terms
$x^2 + 7x + 3x + 21$ leading to
$x^2 + 10x + 21$

(*b*) $x = 2$

11. 25·3 centimetres

12. 126·5 metres

13. 3·45 metres

14. (*a*) 8·69 metres

(*b*) 48°

MATHEMATICS INTERMEDIATE 2 UNITS 1, 2 AND 3 PAPER 1 (NON-CALCULATOR) 2011

1. (a) (i) $Q_2 = 6 \cdot 5$
         (ii) $Q_1 = 5$
         (iii) $Q_3 = 9$

(b)

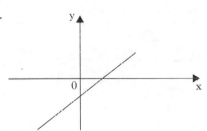

(c) The trains are not as late as the buses **or** the trains are more reliable

2. $6x^2 - 12x - 14$

3. $138°$

4. $3\sqrt{8}$ with evidence

5. To prove $\cos B = \dfrac{5}{9}$

$$\cos B = \frac{a^2 + c^2 - b^2}{2\,a\,c} \text{ (using cosine rule)}$$

$$= \frac{6^2 + 3^2 - 5^2}{2 \times 6 \times 3}$$

$$= \frac{36 + 9 - 25}{36}$$

$$= \frac{20}{36}$$

$$= \frac{5}{9}$$

6. 27

7. $a = 5, b = 4$

8.

9. (a) $(x - 7)(x + 3)$

(b) $7, -3$

(c) $(2, -25)$

10. $\dfrac{4}{5}$

MATHEMATICS INTERMEDIATE 2 UNITS 1, 2 AND 3 PAPER 2 2011

1. $-9/10$

2. £147 900

3. $r = \sqrt{\dfrac{A}{4\pi}}$

4. (a) 106 cubic metres

(b) 17·4 metres

5. 25·1 square metres

6. (a) (i) $\bar{x} = 41$
         (ii) $s = 2 \cdot 1$

(b) Yes, with reasons covering both conditions

7. (a) $24x + 6y = 60$

(b) $20x + 10y = 40$

(c) 25 points

8. $\dfrac{3}{x - 5}$

9. $\dfrac{3 - x}{x\,(x + 1)}$

10. $x = 76$ and $x = 256$

11. 0·2, 1·6

12. 21 centimetres

13. 25·1 millimetres

14. To prove $\dfrac{\sin^2 A}{1 - \sin^2 A} = \tan^2 A$

Left side of equation $= \dfrac{\sin^2 A}{1 - \sin^2 A}$

$$= \frac{\sin^2 A}{\cos^2 A}$$

$$= \tan^2 A$$

$$= \text{right side of equation}$$

Hey! I've done it

Published by Bright Red Publishing Ltd, 6 Stafford Street, Edinburgh, EH3 7AU
Tel: 0131 220 5804, Fax: 0131 220 6710, enquiries: sales@brightredpublishing.co.uk,
www.brightredpublishing.co.uk

Official SQA answers to 978-1-84948-202-8
2007-2011